NOTHING TO FEAR

JESUS WALKS ON WATER

By Marilyn Lashbrook

Illustrated by Chris Sharp

ME TOO!
R E A D E R S

ROPER PRESS, INC.
DALLAS, TEXAS

ME TOO! READERS are designed to help you share the joy of reading with children. They provide a new and fun way to improve a child's reading skills - by practice and example. At the same time, you are teaching your child valuable Bible truths.

Children will learn there is "NOTHING TO FEAR" because Jesus is the loving, powerful Son of God. This book presents the vital truth that Jesus is God - a truth a child must embrace if he is to ward off attacks on faith.

Reading is the key to successful education. Obeying the principles of God's Word opens the door to a successful life. ME TOO! READERS encourage your children in both!

Bold type: Child reads
Regular type: Adult reads
⬣ : Wait for child to respond
♥♥ : Talk about it!

Library of Congress Catalog Card Number: 96-61060
ISBN 0-86606-443-5

Copyright © 1991 by Roper Press, Inc. All Rights Reserved.
Printed in the U.S.A.

Art direction and design by
    Chris Schechner Graphic Design

NOTHING TO FEAR

JESUS WALKS ON WATER

By Marilyn Lashbrook

Illustrated by Chris Sharp

Taken from Matthew 14, Mark 6 and John 7

ME TOO!
R E A D E R S

It was exciting to follow Jesus.

Each day was full of new adventures

for the disciples.

This day was a day of miracles.

Jesus healed sick people.

He made lame people walk.

He made blind people see.

The disciples helped Jesus with the crowds

of needy people. Now the sun was going down,

and the disciples were tired.

Jesus walked the disciples down to the shore. "You go on ahead," Jesus told them. Take the boat back across the sea. I'll come later. I still have things to do here."

The men wanted to know why Jesus would not come with them. They did not want to go without Him.

The disciples were not happy.

They all talked at once.

"How will you come without a boat?" one argued, "It's too far to…"

"It's getting dark!" someone interrupted. "And I'm sure I feel a storm coming"

"Me too!" another piped up.

"Why do you want us to leave?" somebody asked. "How much longer do you need?"

But Jesus was not going to change His mind. He needed time alone to pray.

"Go ahead," He repeated. "I'll catch up with you."

Catch up! Without a boat! How would He do that? ●

The disciples did not understand Jesus' power. Even though they had seen His miracles and heard His teachings, they did not know who He really was.

But they were glad for a chance to sit down and rest. So they pushed the boat into the water and climbed in.

The disciples were tired, but not as tired as they were going to be. A long and frightening night lay ahead.

Slowly the disciples rowed out into the lake. The peaceful sound of water splashing against their boat helped them relax.

They talked about the wonderful things Jesus did. That very day, He had healed sick people and fed hungry people.

Jesus even turned a little boy's lunch into enough food to feed 5000 people. If Jesus could do that, He could do anything!

The disciples looked back toward shore. Families were walking in all directions. It was time for everyone to go home.

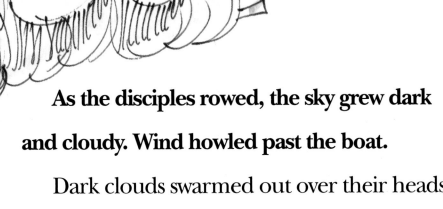

**As the disciples rowed, the sky grew dark
and cloudy. Wind howled past the boat.**

Dark clouds swarmed out over their heads,
and the disciples grew uneasy. There were a lot
of spooky stories about storms and spirits and
sea serpents...and sailors who died at sea.

The weather grew worse. Angry waves tossed the little ship back and forth. The men rowed as hard as they could, but the wind was too strong.

The disciples were held captive in the middle of the lake. The storm was like a great monster, waiting to swallow them alive.

For hours the men tugged at the oars. It was long after midnight now. They were still only halfway across.

Their arms ached but they did not dare stop rowing. What would happen to them if the boat sank? It was three miles to shore — a long swim on a stormy night.

Just then, the disciples saw something scary. Even though they were big, strong brave fishermen, their faces turned pale. Their eyes bulged. Their mouths fell open. They had never seen anything like this before!

"It's a G-G-G-Ghost!" someone stuttered.

They all stared in fright. Closer and closer it came. The disciples were shaking and their hearts were thumping wildly.

Suddenly a friendly voice called out,

"Don't be afraid!"

The disciples held their breath and stared

in fright, "It isn't a ghost! It's Jesus!

He's...He's walking...on the water!"

Peter called out, "Lord, If it is really you, ask me to come to you on the water."

Do you think you would have said that?

"Come." said Jesus.

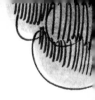

So Peter climbed out of the boat and stood on the water. He did not sink. It was a miracle!

Peter took a step. And another step. This was unbelievable! But it was true. Peter was walking. He was walking on the water. Would you like to do that?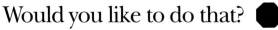

Suddenly Peter noticed the wind. As the waves splashed around his legs, Peter realized how far he was from the boat. The wind seemed to blow his faith away. He was frightened.

Fear was like an anchor pulling Peter down...down...down into the sea. He was sinking fast.

"Lord!" He cried out to Jesus, "Save me!"

Instantly, Jesus reached out and caught him. "O you of little faith!" Jesus said, "Why did you doubt?"

Why do you think Peter stopped trusting Jesus to help him walk on the water?

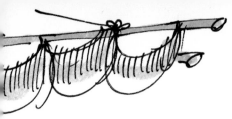

As soon as they climbed into the boat, the wind stopped and the sea calmed. Instantly, the boat was on shore.

One by one the disciples began to understand who Jesus was. He was not just a good man. He was not just a great man. He was God! Jesus was God the Son.

And the disciples fell to their knees and worshipped him. 🖤🖤

ME TOO!
B O O K S

For Ages 2-5

SOMEONE TO LOVE
THE STORY OF CREATION

TWO BY TWO
THE STORY OF NOAH'S FAITH

"I DON'T WANT TO"
THE STORY OF JONAH

"I MAY BE LITTLE"
THE STORY OF DAVID'S GROWTH

"I'LL PRAY ANYWAY"
THE STORY OF DANIEL

WHO NEEDS A BOAT?
THE STORY OF MOSES

"GET LOST LITTLE BROTHER"
THE STORY OF JOSEPH

THE WALL THAT DID NOT FALL
THE STORY OF RAHAB'S FAITH

NO TREE FOR CHRISTMAS
THE STORY OF JESUS' BIRTH

"NOW I SEE"
THE STORY OF THE MAN BORN BLIND

DON'T ROCK THE BOAT!
THE STORY OF THE MIRACULOUS CATCH

OUT ON A LIMB
THE STORY OF ZACCHAEUS

SOWING AND GROWING
THE PARABLE OF THE SOWER AND THE SOILS

DON'T STOP . . . FILL EVERY POT
THE STORY OF THE WIDOW'S OIL

GOOD, BETTER, BEST
THE STORY OF MARY AND MARTHA

GOD'S HAPPY HELPERS
THE STORY OF TABITHA AND FRIENDS

ME TOO!
R E A D E R S

For Ages 5-8

IT'S NOT MY FAULT
MAN'S BIG MISTAKE

GOD, PLEASE SEND FIRE!
ELIJAH AND THE PROPHETS OF BAAL

TOO BAD, AHAB!
NABOTH'S VINEYARD

THE WEAK STRONGMAN
SAMSON

NOTHING TO FEAR
JESUS WALKS ON WATER

THE BEST DAY EVER
THE STORY OF JESUS

THE GREAT SHAKE-UP
MIRACLES IN PHILIPPI

TWO LADS AND A DAD
THE PRODIGAL SON

Available at your local bookstore or from:
Roper Press
4737-A Gretna
Dallas, Texas 75207
1-800-284-0158